ONE VINTAGE

ONE VINTAGE
A YEAR IN THE VINEYARD

CHRIS JONES

Sage Hill Publishing | Los Olivos, California | www.sagehillpublishing.com

Published by Sage Hill Publishing, P.O. Box 434, Los Olivos, California 93441
www.sagehillpublishing.com

ISBN-13: 978-0-9819062-0-1

Library of Congress Control Number: 2008907262

Photographs by author

Edited by Pauline Brand Nelson

Designed by Andrea Russell

Proofread by Kay Thompson Lee

Printed by O'Neil Printing, Phoenix, Arizona

Bookbinding by Roswell Bookbinding, Phoenix, Arizona

First Edition

For Farmer John, Megan and the Crew

Contents

Prelude

In the soil of our Santa Ynez vineyard, sibling vines grow side by side. Though all are rooted in the same gravelly clay loam, some flourish, lush and green, while others seem to struggle, stunted and pale. It is a mystery.

"Viticulture is an art, like practicing medicine," says our friend Paul Hohe, a retired physician and fellow wine grape grower. He is right. At first we rely on technical knowledge, but in the end experience and intuition are our most valuable tools. Nothing is wholly predictable, but we have learned that the elements beyond our control are what make each vintage, like each life, unique.

One Vintage is about one year of farming wine grapes, from bud to harvest: about the everyday realities of working the vineyard, despite exhaustion and loss. It is about how we are healed and restored by that work and by this place, whose seasons reflect the great cycle of life.

Words

BUD:

An undeveloped shoot formed at the base of a leaf, usually protected by scales.

BLOCK:

A section of vineyard, usually with the same soil, vine spacing, rootstock and clones.

CANE:

A one-year-old shoot grown from a bud location.

CANOPY:

The active growing vegetation of the vine.

CATCH WIRE:

A trellis wire that holds the shoots in the desired position.

CLONE:

A group of vines of uniform type, propagated vegetatively from an original mother vine with distinctive varietal characteristics.

CORDON:
A cane that is allowed to remain along a trellis support wire for more than one year, becoming a permanent part of the vine's structure.

COVER CROP:
Vegetation that grows between the vine rows. As well as providing erosion control and a beneficial insect habitat, it improves soil structure and controls vine vigor.

PETIOLE:
A leaf stalk that attaches the leaf blade to the shoot.

SHOOT:
Current season's stem growth that bears leaves and buds.

SPUR:
A portion of the previous year's cane, containing buds, left on the vine at winter pruning.

TRELLIS:
A physical structure that supports the vines.

ONE VINTAGE

Groundwork

The vibrant gold light of summer has changed overnight into the reserved blue of fall. Post harvest is a quiet time, a time of renewal and reflection. I stand on the patio behind our home and look out across the twisted knots of woody vines. Crackling with the first frost, yellow ocher leaves drift to the ground, leaving lonely brown canes clinging to the trellis catch wires.

It is almost seven years since my husband John and I planted this vineyard, the fruition of a dream we had nurtured for twenty years. Like newlyweds, full of naiveté and promise, we christened our new venture Faith Vineyard, for the belief in something of which there is no proof.

The honeymoon bliss lingered for a time. I was happy to have returned to my roots – the round, grassy hills of California's Central Coast, artfully sprinkled with oaks – and it was easy to train and manipulate baby vines in our seven acres of freshly tilled, weed-free soil. But nothing is easy when it has to be done seven thousand times. After bending to remove excess shoots from so many eight-inch plants, I was hot and aching and my bride buzz was gone. Where was the romantic vision of the wine country life I had glimpsed in glossy magazines?

Then the gophers arrived, and the squirrels, and with them came the true realization of what lay ahead of us. With surgical efficiency, the gophers' yellow teeth severed juvenile roots at forty-five degree angles. Thirsty squirrels punctured the irrigation hoses. Vines died. The honeymoon was over; the real adventure was beginning. It was time to roll up our sleeves.

We read viticulture articles, attended seminars, and questioned our gracious friend, Bill Wathen, from Foxen Winery. An accomplished winemaker and farmer, Bill offered us the invaluable gifts of his wisdom and encouragement. The calming effect of his presence and advice reminded me of a time when I had been similarly blessed. Our newborn daughter Megan had arrived – as did our vines – without an instruction manual. Overwhelmed at times by the challenge of new motherhood, I gladly welcomed the advice of my friend Bea.

Just as Bill is a natural farmer, Bea was a natural mother. As her ebony arms embraced my squirming infant and her soft songs soothed, I watched, and marveled, and learned. Bea never judged; she just gently guided and encouraged, and Megan thrived, despite my shortcomings as a mother.

And so did our vines, in spite of our inexperience and mistakes. Three years after planting, in a blur of relief and gratitude, we delivered our first harvest of Sangiovese and Sauvignon Blanc grapes to several Santa Barbara County wineries. It was a momentous occasion – the true fruition of our dream – and it has felt no less momentous with each successive harvest.

Each year, as well, connects me more deeply to this piece of land – its climate, its light, its creatures. I watch its changing face and mark its seasons just as I mark the milestones in the lives of family and friends.

Now the rain comes, the first in six months, and it releases my lingering tension along with the scents of sage, oak and earth. In our Mediterranean climate, cleansing rains begin in November and continue off and on until April, offering hope for next year's crop. Between storms, dormant Valley oaks mimic the sleeping vines: skeletons, lifeless in the dim winter light. The straw-covered hills surrounding the vineyard begin to show hints of green, as resilient bunch grass pokes through last year's dried growth.

Every January, the return of green to these hills signifies the resumption of another vineyard cycle, and speaks to me of life's circularity. I know then that it is time to sharpen the pruning shears and to pull on my boots – pausing first to pluck out last year's piercing grass seeds.

It is time to prepare for the new vintage.

Pruning to Bud Break

Our vineyard year begins with a critical decision: how many buds and spurs to leave on the Sangiovese vines as we prune. Our primary goal is vine balance: maintaining the equilibrium between the leaf canopy and the fruit. As the vintage cycle resumes, we elect to leave two buds per spur and six spurs per cordon on the Sangiovese.

Facing each vine, we cut away the hardened canes – last year's history – leaving sculptured spurs on the cordon for this year's growth. My energy evaporates in the cold; I start to make mistakes. But I have learned that the resilient vines are forgiving of our errors and will reward the time we devote to them, proving a seasoned farmer's saying: "The finest fertilizer is the farmer's footsteps on the vineyard floor."

The early morning is gray on Max's last day. It's easy to love selfless neighbors like our golden-anniversary couple, Max and Nancy. Three weeks ago Max struggled to bake holiday sugar star cookies and shared some with me. He could barely stand, so we sat on the sofa, his frail frame bolstered by pillows. We didn't say much; our hearts and eyes acknowledged that this butter-crumb sweetness was our final communion.

Now as I prune I think of him, drifting towards death in a hospice haze, at home on a hill overlooking our vineyard. Coiled cane tendrils, knotted around the trellis wire, are reluctant to let go. Max, lovingly surrounded by his family, whispers the possibility that he will return as a ladybug, and peacefully passes.

Pruning finished, the clouds recede; a lupine blue sky illuminates the distant Figueroa Mountain.

February brings filaree, my grandmother's scissor plant, to the vineyard's gravel road. Forty-five years ago my maternal grandmother taught me how to create "scissors" by criss-crossing the pale green spikes of the filaree that grew on her Central Coast farm. It is a memory intertwined with others from that place: of flowers everywhere, mice in the hayloft, and grandchildren with root-beer-float mustaches. That farm was where my own dream was born, of living in a place such as this. My daughter, now eighteen and bound for UCLA – her great-grandmother's alma mater – wonders, as my mother did: "Why would anyone want to live on a farm?" She doesn't want to make scissors out of plants.

Birds want to live on our farm. They build nests in the healthiest vines. Ladybugs, reminding me of Max, alight on the cordon's pregnant buds. Creatures are aware of change before we are. Bud break is near. Daffodils bloom under the oaks, filling the shadows with color. Ephemeral rainbows hover over the vineyard, whispering to the vines that it is almost time to awake.

Bud Break to Fruit Set

Spring rains pour life into the soil, nudging our resilient cover crop awake and into a burst of lavish growth. Higher than boot tops now, the lush mix of grasses and flowers brushes our blue jeans as we walk between the vines. California needle grass and poppies, filaree, wild radish and oats, mustard and mallow grow together in a blended community that bustles with bees, wolf spiders, field mice and birds. Even the dark earth is alive, as bacteria and mycorrhizae perform their invisible miracle of helping the vines' roots drink vital nutrients.

In the lengthening days' warmth, the Valley oaks push their emerging chartreuse leaves into the gentle light, softening the silhouettes of winter branches. Soon the vivid green is visible from my kitchen window. Signs of life can be seen on the vines as well, if you look closely: quarter-inch buds, cotton-white, swell on the cordon spurs.

Bud break. Color returns to the Sauvignon Blanc vines in a creeping blush of pink-tinged leaves. It is a risky time, as air temperatures drop on the clear cold nights, and frost is always a threat to the virgin, lettuce-thin foliage. It is no surprise, then, that the first luminous leaves appear on the young replacement vines, sheltered by their protective tubes of thin plastic. Older, seasoned vines contain their exuberance, seeming cautious about accepting the fickle promises of spring.

I share that feeling: excitement at the sight of new growth is tempered by anxiety for tender leaves. My first thought on awakening in March and April is to look outside to the roof and to our wooden picnic table; if there has been frost in the night I will see the dusting of glistening ice crystals there. Is it coincidental that at the beginning of the season, I am reminded that there is a higher power at work?

Unlike many vineyards, we do not have enough well water capacity for frost protection sprinklers, but we do what we can. John mows the cover crop, letting the sun's radiant heat warm the soil, reducing the risk of harm to the burgeoning vines. Frost damage is rare, for which I am thankful. I've seen how thirty minutes of temperatures below 32 degrees can scorch leaves into blackened crisps. Fortunately, we are usually given a second chance, a second growth, and a small crop.

After bud break, the vines become susceptible to mildew. This fungal parasite grows as the daytime temperatures feel more pleasant to us. We begin spraying for protection against mildew and will continue every two to three weeks until veraison, when the sugar accumulating within the grapes will protect the maturing fruit.

Fragile flower-laden shoots burst from the buds' cocooning shells. We want no more than two shoots per spur, so any unnecessary shoots must be pinched off. This allows air and sunlight to penetrate, keeping mildew at bay and enhancing wine flavors. It is a tedious task and must be done soon, before the shoots harden. Like toddlers, immature shoots are pliant and easy to train; older, hardened shoots, like adolescents, are stubborn and prone to snap.

We can't keep up; rambunctious vines overwhelm us. The crew is called in to help. John Krska, our plucky vineyard consultant, provides the competent crew supervised by his right hand man, Jose, whose skill and demeanor belie his young age.

Piling out of an old van, the crew arrives by 6 a.m. They are dressed in layers, bodies bundled so that it's difficult to tell the women from the men. Though their faces are often protected by bright bandanas, their warm brown eyes meet mine. I expect them to begrudge these hours, after the long days they have already worked.

Instead, their laughter rings out through the early morning fog, bringing joy to the vineyard and me. How do they sing while working, when I'm exhausted by lunchtime? Do they have the key to inner happiness and contentment? I could not farm without them, and am grateful when I hear the van's tires crunching the gravel road to our red barn.

Making a tough job look easy, the twelve professionals finish shoot thinning in three days. They will return for one more day, to tuck foliage upright between catch wires.

They arrive early the next morning – I have just poured myself a cup of hot tea and lemon. Their familiar voices drift through my kitchen window with the dawn fog; its sea smoke mingles with the steam from my cup. The crew is already shoot positioning, ensuring that developing leaves and clusters do not overshadow one another, and that tender canes do not break.

Halfway through the day, a reminder that our vines serve other purposes to other creatures: hidden behind shoots on a Sangiovese cordon, a twig nest gives precarious shelter to three small sparrows.

The next day's dawn draws me back to the newborns' nest. During the night it has been damaged, and now – a mother's greatest fear – it is empty. Perhaps it was the wind; perhaps an animal has unmade this nest, I cannot tell. But the result is the same: perched on a vine post not far from her broken home, the mother sings her guilt and sorrow inconsolably. Frustrated by my inability to comfort her, I finish shoot positioning, knowing that the next gust of wind could blow my own efforts into disarray.

Another pass through the vineyard, this time to knock off new Sauvignon Blanc suckers growing from the vine trunk; another day of bending, straightening and endless repetition. A flash of color breaks the monotony: an exuberant red-stemmed rootstock sucker is growing close to the soil. Grape clones are grafted onto rootstock derived from a native phylloxera-resistant grapevine. At least ten different rootstocks are available to grape growers, who make their selections after weighing factors such as the root's vigor, drought tolerance, and resistance to pests; the quality of the vineyard soil; and the desired wine flavor profiles.

Each spring we replace any vines lost to disease, gopher or tractor damage with vines shipped from a grapevine nursery. The nursery propagates our vines by grafting our chosen rootstock, 101-14 and 5C, with a scion of our varietal, Sauvignon Blanc or Sangiovese. We selected our varietals after considering which grapes would be most likely to produce fine wines in our vineyard environment, or *terroir*, and which wines we enjoy with our meals.

We chose the Sangiovese, an Italian varietal, in honor of Lou Chelini, a retired Cleveland schoolteacher turned wine merchant. Twenty years ago, Lou's enthusiasm for life, his kindness and his non-intimidating Monday night wine classes opened our eyes to a world beyond Chardonnay, Cabernet Sauvignon and Monday night football. Here's to you, Lou: thank you.

Shy, honey-fragrant, self-pollinating grape flowers epitomize both the beauty and the challenge of grape growing. Each flower contains almost 20,000 pollen grains, a quantity that seems ample, even lavish; but the flowers are particular about the environment for successful pollination. It must not be too cool – no chillier than 59°F – or too damp, or too windy. In addition, the plant's chemistry and hormones must be in balance.

During fertilization, five small white petals detach themselves at the base of the flower and lift off as a cap to expose the anther and pistil. A cloud of pollen then releases from the anther and falls on the upper surface of the pistil. After fertilization and fruit set, a small black scar remains on the polar end of the young berry.

Viticulture researchers measure and quantify the complexities of grapevine development; greenhorn farmers try to figure out what a "normal" year looks like. But experience teaches us that the whole process is a delicate mystery; how it unfolds depends mostly on the daily miracles taking place in the vines themselves, and on the occasional surprises nature has up her sleeve. We have less control than we would like to think. There is no "normal" year.

Last year, a bitter wind blew through our vineyard, felling an ancient Valley oak that had shown no signs of disease. The massive trunk lay across three vine rows, exposing a core that could no longer support the weight of its copious canopy. The same powerful wind prevented most of our petite Sauvignon Blanc flowers from developing completely. The term for this is "shatter," and it perfectly describes what happens to the flower if it does not pollinate: it dries up and falls apart. As the word implies, shatter is bad news to a grape grower: last year's crop of Sauvignon Blanc was very light. We are paid by the ton.

This year, shatter sweeps, not into the vineyard, but into our comfortable lives. Our daughter Megan, a high school senior, is diagnosed with a bone tumor. My father, heartbroken and lost after my mother's death, returns to the hospital to ease his pain. John's employer, a now bankrupt airline, cuts his salary and eliminates his pension. Will we be able to stay and farm our dream? In the midst of so many devastating blows, it is hard to have faith, hard not to ask: why me?

And yet, by grace, unconditional love envelops and strengthens me. Prayer and hope combat my helplessness. I walk through the vineyard to the spot where the oak stood, and begin to stack logs that have been cut for the fireplace. Larger planks have already been taken and milled for a table John will build. I wonder: do we, like the oak, become something different through upheaval, possibly something more?

Set to Veraison

Like rebellious teenagers in the midst of a growth spurt, the vines stretch past the last catch wire. In late June, when the midday heat is strong, I walk between the ten-foot-high rows. The vigorous canopy growth creates a soft green light – a clear reminder that we must act soon if we are to maintain vine balance. Sometimes things just seem to grow too fast. In farming, as in parenting, there are days when I feel I am in over my head.

It is time to start hedging. This is necessary for good fruit; removing the active growing tips and reducing the ratio of leaf surface to crop load restores the vines to hormonal and chemical equilibrium. Hedging – or topping – also creates the uniform row height needed for bird net application. Still, this is one of those times when I'm jealous of the "big boys" – the larger vineyards with their mechanical hedgers.

John and I have our own unconventional method of topping. In the early evening, when the heat is less intense, I drive the John Deere Gator up one row and down the next. Behind my yellow seat in the six-wheeled ATV, bracing himself on a chair that has been clamped to the vehicle, my husband stands ready for battle. A fuming generator powers the electric hedger that he wields like a sword, slashing the shoots that reach past the last catch wire. The cut foliage smells of grapes, and the air fills with fragrance as it falls. Less pleasant are the leafhoppers – insects that feed on leaf cells. Stirred up by the topping, they feed on me instead.

Stiff-necked and bitten, I watch the sun slip into the purple-gold horizon. "Where's the romance?" I ask John. "Shouldn't we be toasting the sunset with a crisp Sauvignon Blanc, tasting of lemongrass and passion fruit?"

"Go right ahead," he snaps. Exhausted, he tucks our homemade hedger into the barn for the night. Harvest is still at least two months away.

There are too many leaves around the fruit zone. In order to ripen, the pea-sized berries need sun flecks. The crew returns to pull leaves. In the southeast corner of the vineyard – block two – growing under a lush Sauvignon Blanc vine, we come across a tomato plant bearing a single ripe tomato. It is a memento from another hot day, when a worker returned to this shady spot under the vine's canopy to enjoy his lunch of hot tortillas and tomatoes. This is a favorite meal among the workers at midday: fresh tomato, a squeeze of lime and spiced meat piled on a tortilla, sizzling hot from a portable butane burner.

Heat ripples the air in the cloudless afternoon. Jose, the crew's intuitive foreman, makes a suggestion. "Be quiet for five minutes. Listen to the rain. Cool down." Chatter fades and I begin to hear raindrops. It is the sound of the plucking of the leaves. It feels cooler.

During our dry summers, drip irrigation – one of the few things we can control – helps maintain vine balance. Too much water creates an abundance of leaves and less fruit; not enough water weakens the vine, making it more susceptible to disease, berry collapse and unripe fruit. John begins the first irrigation when the petiole angles drop, and soil moisture instruments indicate that it's time. He calculates the amount of water each plant receives by using a formula accounting for evapotranspiration, or ET.

Enormous vines appear at the end of some rows. Digging three feet under the plants, we discover that the gorged vines have been receiving unlimited water through holes in the underground irrigation line – holes gnawed by gophers.

Maybe even this is beyond our control.

Veraison to Harvest

In July, the hard green Sauvignon Blanc and Sangiovese berries begin to prepare for harvest. Entering veraison, they stop expanding, begin to soften and accumulate sugar. Within each cluster, in no particular order, individual berries fill with sugar one after the other. Sangiovese berries, like all red varieties, take their turns changing from green to pink to purple.

At veraison the fruit becomes edible to the birds. As if in response to a signal, hungry starlings congregate in huge black clouds – called dragons – that soar and wheel overhead. The crew scurries to cover the vine rows with bird nets. When the nets are in place, the Gator no longer fits between rows, so John makes his irrigation rounds on his mountain bike, riding up and down the rows in ninety-degree heat.

Irrigation management is part hard labor: cleaning plugged emitters, and patching leaks in lines that have been gnawed by persistent squirrels. But it is also an art, the key to which, once again, is balance. John's goal now is to maintain the vine's canopy, while convincing the plant that it is time to concentrate on grape flavor development. When eighty percent of the Sangiovese clusters are purple, green immature clusters are cut away to prevent vegetative, unripe flavors in the wine.

With veraison, also, comes the grapes' own resistance to powdery mildew. It is a relief for us to be finished with the early morning spraying; it is even more of a relief to our patient neighbors, who have listened every two to three weeks since bud break to the whine of the spray rig.

Crickets and frogs sing me to sleep on summer evenings, and in the blue-black night the diligent owls hoot and hunt. Some nights we are wakened by the howling and yipping of coyotes, who slip in among the vines to party. The sweet grapes under their nets are vulnerable; the coyotes gobble them up, showing a marked preference for red over white, and leave a mess. Sly raccoons arrive unannounced, eat, and slink away, leaving no sign except their footprints in the warm powdery soil.

The fence keeps out the deer and wild pigs, but there are other threats that respect no such barrier. Mealy bugs and glassy-winged sharpshooters land uninvited on one neighbor's vines. Will they come to ours? The canopy is tiring and I see the leaves are curling. Is it a virus, or just old age? I wish there were a fence that could keep worry at bay, but it is a frequent companion at this time of year.

In midsummer, our everyday concerns are thrown into sharp perspective when we receive bad news about our dear friend, Michael. He is someone who never worries, who shares a contagious *joie de vivre* that uplifts one and all. Early on August 17th, I am startled awake by a telephone call. It is Patti, Michael's wife, who calls to tell us that Michael has had a severe stroke in Buenos Aires and is now critically ill. It is 6 a.m., the coldest hour of the day, and I struggle for words. I remember the days after my mother's death, and the inexplicable sense I had of being surrounded by warm love. I pray that Patti will know that same feeling now.

Amid tragedy, life – ordinary, oblivious – continues. Bill Wathen stops by on his way to the winery to discuss dropping more Sangiovese clusters, while Tommy, his gregarious rat terrier, happily digs, snooping for squirrels. Life, like wine, is not static.

The canes are lignifying, maturing, turning from green to brown. I gather our first grape sample: one Sauvignon Blanc berry from every third plant in four random rows. The ripest berries pull easily from the rachis, or stem; I drop the samples into plastic sandwich bags and take them into the kitchen.

After crushing the grapes and tasting the juice, I look at the seeds to estimate what percentage of them has turned brown. Then I measure sugar accumulation. I use a refractometer, placing two or three drops of fresh juice on the surface of its main prism. A beam of light penetrates the liquid, searching for the concentration of sucrose in the water. The percentage of sugar, or degrees Brix, has reached eighteen. This confirms the results of my tasting, as my mouth puckers in response to the acidic juice: the grapes need more time on the vine.

Every week from now on, John or I will sample the grapes this way, and report the results to our winemakers. We will note carefully all the markers of maturity: the proportion of seeds turning brown and hard, the fall in acidity, the rise in sugar, and the emergence of pronounced flavors. Eventually, the winemakers will come to the vineyard themselves, usually at least two weeks before harvest, to gather and test their own samples, to decide when to pick.

End of August. Temperatures climb; the sugar increases in the Sauvignon Blanc one degree per week. Not all berries ripen in the Sangiovese. Some shrivel, pinched and crowded by their neighbors. Tightly clustered berries are more susceptible to rot, but there is nothing we can do about that now. Yellow jackets dine and dance on the amber globules of the Sauvignon Blanc that are starting to dehydrate and lose weight. Plump, polished acorns lie in the dust by the vineyard's gate.

These last slow days before harvest are heavy with tension, and full of questions. Is the fruit at its peak? What is the weather forecast? Will the crew be available when we need them? Is the press ready? We are anxious to be relieved of our duty.

The hummingbirds, like us, begin to bicker.

Just before harvest, Megan and I escape to London. She has recovered from her surgery, and loves the stimulation of the cosmopolitan culture, the black taxis, the pulsating crowds and the pomp. Unlike home, London is vibrant, not boring – and Megan is of legal drinking age.

One evening in Knightsbridge, we push open the wooden door of an Italian restaurant and are instantly enveloped by its rich atmosphere. British reserve is left outside; we are greeted by waves of garlic and the genial welcome of a waiter for whom the work of the restaurant is not just a job, it is a calling. He shows us to our candlelit table for two. While we drink Italian Chianti – made from Sangiovese grapes – we are surrounded by all ages, mostly locals, who are unaware that in their midst a milestone is being passed. A child is becoming a young woman, and a mother is letting go.

Suddenly, I am flooded with memories of other milestones, all the "firsts" in the life of my daughter whom I regard now with such pride, and love. I try to blink away the tears. She notices, and her eyes – clear, piercing sapphires – hold a question: "why?"

"It's hormones, and jet lag," I lie, unable to say how sacred and fleeting is this sweet spot. A moment like this is my motivation: to know that wine made from our grapes is shared by people at times like this, times of celebration and companionship; to know that it enhances their meals and enriches their lives. This is all that I need.

I return to the place of my inspiration: our vineyard, with its subtle beauty.

The Sauvignon Blanc juice climbs to twenty-three degrees Brix and tastes of green apple, guava and lime. If we need further evidence that the moment for picking is finally here, we get it in the form of tarantulas, who arrive in search of mates. They are always our harbingers of harvest.

The bird nets are raised, and on September 15th the first harvest of this vintage begins.

In earlier years, friends would join us at harvest to pick. Not any more. "Too busy," most say, the novelty worn off. Instead, our trusted crew's gloved hands cradle, clip and drop each Sauvignon Blanc cluster into five gallon buckets. Brimming buckets wait under vines for the runner, who empties the green-gold berries with a gentle thud into white plastic bins, four-foot square. Sputtering diesel, the tractor pulls the two half-ton-capacity containers down the row, ahead of the crew.

By the first hour's end we know how the day will go, what the rhythm of this harvest will be. The more leaves there are, the more difficult it is to remove the grape clusters. If clusters are small and numerous, the process will be slow. After one hour we will know how fast the harvest will be, and how much it will probably yield.

Today the bins fill too quickly, twice as fast as predicted, twice the anticipated yield. Last year's yield was less than one ton per acre; this year it will be almost eight tons. Rather than being grateful, I worry. Will the fruit retain its intensity? Will the winemakers take the unexpected bounty?

A week later, our final Sauvignon Blanc harvest begins in a chilly fog. We have the help of two crews: fourteen people pick one ton per hour, cluster after cluster, vine after vine, row after row.   By the end of the day, the temperature has risen fifty degrees and fatigue overwhelms my joy.   All I want is a cold beer.

On October 11th, wind rattles the finished Sauvignon Blanc leaves. Summer is gone. It is barely daybreak – 6:15 – when the crew arrives to harvest the Sangiovese. Night-chilled purple-black clusters fly into the half-ton bins. My frozen fingers pick out leaves and twigs – any material other than grapes, or "mog," as the winemakers call it. By 10:30 we are finished. The workers sip sodas in the barn's shade, watching as fourteen full bins are forklifted onto a flatbed truck to be driven to the winery. Each ton will yield sixty cases of wine.

John drives Foxen's wheezing truck, laden with cool fruit, arriving at the winery by noon. Clamoring yellow jackets claim the crop as it waits to be weighed. High above Bill Wathen and his crew, a golden eagle floats, lingering, as if blessing the harvest that is leaving our care. The clusters are mechanically destemmed, and the berries are dumped into a steel fermenter. Bill, with his palette of yeast, mixes the fermenting juice.

It will be two more years before this wine – this transformation of nature into art, this result of so much human collaboration, this rich dark liquid tasting of strawberry, guava and pomegranate – is released.

After Harvest

The grapes are gone. Bird nets and boots are stored. The vines are dormant. Roots are growing, gulping the last irrigation before the rains come. Worn out oak leaves take one last swirl by the red barn, before they drift away. I bring in some of the logs cut from our fallen oak, and light the first fire of the season. Warmth and grace embrace me as the ancient wood releases 250 years of accumulated sunshine.

In December and January, John and I meet our winemakers at their wineries to taste our vineyard's new vintage. The winemaker siphons a sample of Sauvignon Blanc from the chilled stainless steel tank. I sip in silence, awed by our vineyard's zestful green-gold miracle. The furrow in John's brow clears: the wine exceeds his expectations. Surrounded by the past – vintages resting in oak barrels and stainless steel – we discuss the future, and seal next year's grape contract with a handshake.

So we go on. Now and then we contemplate doing things differently. Some wine critics prefer powerful trophy wines to compatible, food-friendly wines. We could alter our farming practices, and possibly appeal to those critics. It is a tempting prospect, but in the end we come back to our present course: farming holistically, manipulating as little as possible, seeking balance. With the support of our crew we persevere, running the farm as we planned, back when it was only our dream.

That dream, now granted, has not been as I envisioned it; nor has it been easy. Always challenging, always changing, the life of the vineyard is a mystery that tenderly teaches and touches my soul.

Postlude

It is a cloudless spring morning, in the following year. The vines are flowering and the buds of another year's vintage are forming. I am looking at a swath of daffodils nodding in the sun, but these are not the daffodils that grow under my oaks. We have come to a little country cemetery, not far from my parents' Central Coast birthplace. Wildflowers soften the hard outlines of headstones – some dating back to the nineteenth century.

The song of meadowlarks mingles with a bagpipe's plaintive tune. Megan, now healed, helps bury her grandfather's ashes next to my mother's, in a box lovingly crafted by John from the fallen oak's wood.

Life's rhythm continues.

Information on where to purchase additional copies of

ONE VINTAGE may be obtained at sagehillpublishing.com.